THE OFFICIAL
QUEEN OF THE SOUTH
QUIZ BOOK

THE OFFICIAL QUEEN OF THE SOUTH QUIZ BOOK

800 Questions on The Doonhamers

Compiled by
Chris Cowlin and Kevin Snelgrove

Foreword by Davie Rae

APEX PUBLISHING LTD

Hardback first published in 2010 by

Apex Publishing Ltd
PO Box 7086, Clacton on Sea, Essex, CO15 5WN, England
www.apexpublishing.co.uk

Copyright © 2010 by Chris Cowlin and Kevin Snelgrove
The authors have asserted their moral rights

British Library Cataloguing-in-Publication Data
A catalogue record for this book
is available from the British Library

ISBN HARDBACK: 1-906358-82-6   978-1-906358-82-2

Typeset in 10.5pt Chianti Bdlt Win95BT

Cover Design: Siobhan Smith

Printed and bound in Great Britain by the
MPG Books Group, Bodmin and King's Lynn

Author's Note:
Please can you contact me: ChrisCowlin@btconnect.com if you find any mistakes/errors in this book as I would like to put them right on any future reprints of this book. I would also like to hear from Queens fans who have enjoyed the test! For more information on me and my books please look at: **www.ChrisCowlin.com**

This book is an official product of Queen of the South Football Club

We would like to dedicate this book to:

All the players and staff who have worked for the club during their history.

FOREWORD

On 21st March 2009 Queen of the South Football Club celebrated their 90th anniversary and it was good to see 25 former players at Palmerston Park to pay tribute.

It was a great honour for me to be Chairman on such an historic occasion and it was nice to meet up again with two of my boyhood heroes, Jim Patterson and Bobby Black.

I still vividly recall my first ever visit to Palmerston! I was only 11 at the time and my granny walked me four miles from Hightae village to Lochmaben to catch the service bus to Dumfries. Eight miles and about an hour later we arrived at the park and Queens beat Partick Thistle 8-2 that afternoon.

I still remember that date, 28th August 1948, and our Scottish internationalist Billy Houliston netted five goals.

The following season Queens reached the semi-final of the Scottish Cup at Hampden, but after drawing 1-1 with Rangers, we lost the replay.

Little did I realise that 58 years later I'd be back at Hampden as Chairman to watch my team play Rangers again. But this time it was in the final itself! We lost 3-2 in front of 48,821 fans but I was very proud of the lads.

That was a tremendous game but, if I was honest, I enjoyed the 4-3 victory in the semi-final against Aberdeen even better.

In my younger days I was a regular Queens' supporter but as the years rolled by I had to supervise my three farms and couldn't get to Palmerston quite so much. However in 2002 the then Chairman Ronnie Bradford asked me to join the Board of Directors. I said 'yes' and in November 2003 I was appointed Chairman which I deemed a great honour.

Before this book went to press I was allowed a sneak preview and found it interesting reading. Some of the questions had even me baffled and I would recommend it to all Queens' fans - young and old.

Davie Rae
Queen of the South Football Club (Chairman)

INTRODUCTION

I would first of all like to thank Davie Rae for writing the foreword to this book. I am very grateful for his help on this project.

I would also like to thank all the people who have provided a comment and/or review on this book (these can be found at the back of the book).

I would also like to thank Bill Goldie at Queen of the South Football Club for all his help and Bruce Wright for proof reading the book.

I hope you enjoy this book. Hopefully it should bring back some wonderful memories!

It was great working with Kevin Snelgrove again, between us I hope we have given you a selection of easy, medium and hard questions.

In closing, I would like to thank all my friends and family for encouraging me to complete this book.

Best wishes
Chris Cowlin

www.apexpublishing.co.uk

CLUB HISTORY

1. In which year was the club formed – 1918, 1919 or 1920?

2. Which Queen of the South player scored a club record of 37 goals during the 1927/28 season?

3. In which competition did Queen of the South play for the first time in their history during 2008?

4. In which season did the club finish as Division Three runners-up – 1922/23, 1923/24 or 1924/25?

5. What is the club's nickname?

6. Can you name the motto that appears on the club crest?

7. In which year did the club first win the Potts Cup?

8. Can you name the club's longest-serving player, playing for them from1960 to 1981?

9. Against which team did the club play in the first ever Scottish League match under floodlights on 7 March 1956 away from home?

10. Can you name the club mascot, a human-sized border collie?

ALLAN BALL

11. In what position did Allan play during his playing days?

12. What was Allan's nickname whilst a Doonhamers player?

13. How many competitive games did Allan play for Queen of the South – 713, 731 or 771?

14. True or false: Allan is an honorary director at Queen of the South?

15. In what year did Allan sign for Queen of the South?

16. Which Queens manager handed Allan his club debut?

17. Against which club did Allan make his Queens debut in a 6-3 defeat?

18. True or false: Allan only ever received one yellow card during his Queens playing career?

19. For which Scottish team did Allan play after he left Queen of the South?

20. Against which two teams did Allan play in his two testimonial matches, one in the 1970s and one in the 1980s?

MANAGERS – 1

Match up the manager with the year he took charge of The Doonhamers

21.	Billy McLaren	1967
22.	Derek Frye	1973
23.	Mike Jackson	1937
24.	Willie Ferguson	1979
25.	George Herd	1991
26.	Billy Little	1992
27.	John Connolly	1993
28.	Ally McLeod	1986
29.	Willie McLean	1980
30.	Jackie Husband	2000

GORDON CHISHOLM

31. In which year was Gordon born in Glasgow – 1959, 1960 or 1961?

32. What was Gordon's playing position during his playing days?

33. For which Scottish team did Gordon sign when he left Sunderland in 1985?

34. Gordon was appointed manager of which club in 2005?

35. To whom was Gordon assistant manager at Queen of the South before being named manager in 2007?

36. To what position in the Scottish First Division did Gordon guide the club during his first season in charge, 2007/08?

37. Who was The Doonhamers' chairman when Gordon was appointed as club manager?

38. True or false: Gordon had to wait until his sixth competitive match in charge before Queen of the South won a game?

39. For which Scottish team did Gordon play between 1987 and 1992?

40. To what position in the Scottish First Division did Gordon guide Queen of the South during the 2008/09 season?

2009/10

41. In which position in the League did Queens finish – 3rd, 4th or 5th?

42. With which team did Queens share a 2-2 away draw on Boxing Day 2009?

43. Can you name the three scorers which scored for Queens in the 3-0 home League win against Raith Rovers during April 2010?

44. Which forward finished the clubs highest League scorer with 12 goals?

45. True or false: Queen of the South only played one League match during January 2010?

46. What was the score when Queens played Ayr United in the League at Palmerston Park during February 2010?

47. Which midfielder scored a brace for the club in the 3-3 away draw against Greenock Morton during April 2010?

48. How many of the clubs 36 League matches did they win – 15, 18 or 21?

49. True or false: Queens were unbeaten in their first four League matches, all played during August 2009?

50. Which midfielder scored a brace for the club in the 4-1 away win at Dunfermline Athletic during September 2009?

LEGENDS – 1

Rearrange the letters to reveal the name of a club legend

51.   NAYD MOONTHS

52.   ILILEW AVEGAS

53.   CEIKJA ASKEO

54.   EGEGRO MOTHLAIN

55.   VADE LADYHAIL

56.   ROGGEE RAMF

57.   BYBBO CLABK

58.   RIVO AIDSROB

59.   BOBNY CRAKL

60.   MIMJY BIGNINN

PLAYER OF THE YEAR – 1

Match up the player with the year he won the award

61.	Steve Bowey	1977
62.	Allan Ball	1986
63.	Andy Thomson	1997
64.	Peter Weatherson	1992
65.	Derek Townsley	2004
66.	Crawford Boyd	1976
67.	David Mathieson	1994
68.	Jimmy Robertson	1999
69.	Bobby Parker	1979
70.	Tommy O'Hara	2001

LEAGUE POSITIONS – 1

Match up the season with the club's finishing position in the League

71.	2008/09	1st in Division Two
72.	2007/08	8th in Division One
73.	2006/07	5th in Division Two
74.	2005/06	5th in Division One
75.	2004/05	6th in Division Two
76.	2003/04	9th in Division Two
77.	2002/03	4th in Division One
78.	2001/02	5th in Division One
79.	2000/01	4th in Division One
80.	1999/2000	8th in Division One

2008/09

81. What was the score when Clyde visited Palmerston Park during April 2009, giving Queens' their record victory of the season?

82. Following on from the previous question, which striker scored four goals in the game for Queen of the South?

83. Which midfielder scored six League goals during this season?

84. Who finished as the club's highest League scorer with 23 goals in his 30 starts and 2 substitute appearances?

85. Which midfielder did The Doonhamers sign from Inverness Caledonian Thistle during December 2008?

86. From which club did The Doonhamers sign David Weatherston during August 2008?

87. Who managed Queens during this season?

88. How many of their 36 League games did Queens win during this season – 10, 11 or 12?

89. Who scored a 90th-minute winner against St Johnstone in a 3-2 away League win during April 2009?

90. Which two strikers scored braces in a 6-1 home League win during October 2008?

UEFA CUP – AUGUST 2008

91.   Against which team did Queens play in the UEFA Cup on their European debut?

92.   What was the score in Queens' first European match, played at Excelsior Stadium, Airdrie, on 14 August 2008?

93.   Following on from the previous question, what nationality were the winners?

94.   What was the attendance at Excelsior Stadium, Airdrie, in the second qualifying first leg - 4,406, 5,406 or 6,406?

95.   Who scored Queens' goal after 28 minutes at Excelsior Stadium, Airdrie, in the second qualifying first leg match - the first ever European goal in the club's history?

96.   Who scored a superb 30-yard free kick in the second minute in the second qualifying second leg?

97.   What was the score in the second qualifying second leg, played away from home?

98.   Which midfielder was the only Queens player to be booked in the second qualifying second leg?

99.   From which country was referee Tony Chapron, who took charge of the second qualifying second leg?

100.   Can you name the home ground of Queens' opponents?

CLUB RECORDS

101. Who beat Queens 10-2 in Division One during December 1962, a record club defeat?

102. What is Queen of the South's record attendance, in a game against Hearts in the Scottish Cup during February 1952 - 26,552, 27,552 or 28,552?

103. For how much did Queens sell Andy Thomson in 1994, when he became the club's record transfer?

104. In which season did the club win the Bell's Scottish Football League Angels Award?

105. With what record number of points at the end of a season did Queens finish under the 3 points for a win system, achieved in Division 2 during 2001/02?

106. Who scored a record 41 goals in a season for Queens during 1931/32?

107. Who won the Second Division Manager of the Season award at the end of the 2001/02 season?

108. Against which club did Queen of the South record their record victory, an 11-1 Scottish FA Cup win during January 1932?

109. With what record number of points at the end of a season did Queens finish under the 2 points for a win system, achieved in Division 2 during 1985/86?

110. Who remains the record scorer in the club's history, with 251 goals in 462 appearances between 1949 and 1963?

DIVISION TWO CHAMPIONS – 2001/02

111. Which Queens manager guided the club to this success?

112. By how many points were Queen of the South clear at the top, with Alloa Athletic finishing in 2nd position in the table?

113. Which Queens midfielder finished as the club's highest League scorer this season, with 19 goals?

114. Which team did The Doonhamers beat 6-5 in the League at home during February 2002?

115. Which team did Queens beat 4-0 away from home in the League during September 2001, with John O'Neil scoring a brace in the game?

116. True or false: Queens failed to win their first three League matches of the season?

117. Which team did The Doonhamers beat 4-0 at Palmerston Park on 27 April 2002, with Peter Weatherson scoring a brace in the game?

118. Can you name the striker that scored 16 League goals during this season?

119. Which defender did Queens sign from Alloa during January 2002?

120. How many of their 36 League matches did Queens win – 20, 22 or 24?

QUEENS V. RANGERS

121. Who scored Queens' goal against Rangers in a 2-1 home defeat in the Scottish League Cup third round during September 2009?

122. The sides first met in Division One during the 1933/34 season, but which team won both games, home and away?

123. True or false: Queens' first ever win in the history of the club against Rangers was in the Scottish FA Cup during January 1937 winning 1-0?

124. What was the aggregate score over two legs when the sides met in the Scottish League Cup second round during August 1983?

125. True or false: the sides did not meet in any competition during the 1990s?

126. What was the score when the sides met in the Scottish League Cup semi-final during October 1960 – 7-0 to Rangers, 7-7 draw or 7-0 to Queens?

127. True or false: Queens achieved a double over Rangers, beating them both at home and away, during the 1953/54 League season?

128. For how many years had the sides not met in a competitive competition prior to playing in the Scottish FA Cup final in May 2008?

129. What was the score when Queens met Rangers in the League at home in the 1957/58 season?

130. True or false: the sides met in both the League Cup and Scottish FA Cup during the 1975/76 season?

2002/03

131. Can you name the three goalkeepers that played for Queens during this season?

132. Which team did The Doonhamers beat 1-0 away on the last day of the League season?

133. Following on from the previous question, who scored the only goal for Queens?

134. Which midfielder scored Queens' equaliser in a 2-2 away draw against St Mirren during February 2003?

135. Which striker scored a brace for Queens in a 3-3 away draw with Alloa during January 2003?

136. Which forward signed for Queens from Ayr United during July 2002?

137. Which team did Queens beat 2-1 at home on the opening day of the League season, with midfielder Eric Paton scoring the winning goal?

138. True or false: Queens were unbeaten in all League matches during October 2002?

139. How many of their 36 League games did Queens win – 10, 11 or 12?

140. Which midfielder scored nine League goals for Queens, finishing as the club's highest scorer this season?

IVOR BROADIS

141. What is Ivor's middle name – Arthur, Albert or Archie?

142. How many goals did Ivor score in his 14 full international matches for England – 4, 6 or 8?

143. True or false: in 1946, at the age of 23, Ivor was the youngest person to be appointed as player/manager in the English Football League?

144. In what position did Ivor play during his playing days?

145. Ivor was born on 18 December in which year – 1921, 1922 or 1923?

146. How many League appearances did Ivor make for The Doonhamers – 43, 53 or 63?

147. From which club did Ivor join Queen of the South in 1959?

148. How many League goals did Ivor score for The Doonhamers – 15, 20 or 25?

149. What is Ivor's real first name?

150. What job did Ivor take up when he retired from football?

JIMMY BINNING

151. Jimmy was born on 25 July in which year – 1927, 1928 or 1929?

152. In 1951 Jimmy made his Doonhamers debut in a pre-season St Mungo Cup 3-0 win against which club?

153. How many senior games did Jimmy play for Queen of the South – 188, 288 or 388?

154. In what position did Jimmy play?

155. From which club did Jimmy sign to join Queen of the South in 1951?

156. True or false: Jimmy was selected for the 22-man Scottish squad for the FIFA 1954 World Cup but stayed at home on standby?

157. Which Queen of the South manager signed Jimmy in 1951?

158. Jimmy made his international debut for Scotland in 1954, but who were the opponents?

159. Following on from question 155, how many goals did Jimmy score in his 84 appearances for this club – 6, 16 or 26?

160. In Jimmy's first full season with Queen of the South, in what position did they finish in the top-flight League in 1952?

POSITIONS THEY PLAYED – 1

Match up the player with his playing position

161.	Billy Halliday	Centre half
162.	Graeme Robertson	Striker
163.	Andy Goram	Defender
164.	Chris Balderstone	Centre forward
165.	David Craig	Midfielder
166.	Willie Telfer	Goalkeeper
167.	Bobby Shearer	Inside left
168.	Jimmy Brown	Right back
169.	Billy Findlay	Centre back/Midfielder
170.	Ken Eadie	Fullback

PLAYING YEARS AT THE CLUB – 1

Match up the player with his time at the club

171.	Willie Telfer	2001-07
172.	Andy Aitken (first spell)	1937-38
173.	Billy Houliston	1960-81
174.	Tommy Bryce (second spell)	1996-2004
175.	Willie Gibson	1949-50
176.	Jimmy Brown	1994-98
177.	Jimmy Robertson (first spell)	1949-63
178.	Jim Patterson	1960-61
179.	Iain McChesney	1945-52
180.	George Hamilton	1980-87

TOP APPEARANCES

Match up the player with the number of appearances he made for the club

181.	Jim Kerr	431
182.	Iain McChesney	462
183.	Willie Savage	400
184.	Dougie Sharpe	731
185.	Allan Ball	615
186.	Alan Davidson	457
187.	Roy Henderson	403
188.	Jim Patterson	364
189.	Jimmy Robertson	381
190.	Jackie Oakes	369

QUEENS V. GREENOCK MORTON

191.   Which Queens forward scored the club's winning goal in a 2-1 League away win during December 2009?

192.   How many of the sides' four League meetings during the 2008/09 season ended in draws?

193.   Which striker scored a League hat-trick against Morton in a 3-0 away win during January 2008?

194.   True or false: Greenock Morton beat Queens in all four League meetings during the 1986/87 season?

195.   What was the score when the sides met in the Scottish FA Cup first round at Cappielow Park during November 2001?

196.   The clubs met five times during the 1990s, four times in the League and once in the Scottish League Challenge Cup, with Queens achieving how many wins?

197.   Which former Queens player scored a brace against The Doonhamers in a 2-2 League draw at Cappielow Park during January 2009?

198.   True or false: the clubs did not meet in the League during the 1950s?

199.   In which season did the sides first meet – 1926/27, 1927/28 or 1928/29?

200.   In which competition did the sides meet during the 2002/03 season, resulting in a 1-0 Queens home win?

LEAGUE POSITIONS – 2

*Match up the season with the club's finishing
position in the League*

201.	1998/99	10th in Division Two
202.	1997/98	11th in Division Two
203.	1996/97	12th in Division Two
204.	1995/96	4th in Division Two
205.	1994/95	10th in Division Two
206.	1993/94	4th in Division Two
207.	1992/93	7th in Division Two
208.	1991/92	7th in Division Two
209.	1990/91	5th in Division Two
210.	1989/90	5th in Division Two

2007/08

211. With how many League goals did Stephen Dobbie finish the season, after 29 starts and 7 substitute appearances?

212. Which midfielder did Queens sign from Clyde during August 2007?

213. Which club did Queens beat on Boxing Day 2007 in a 2-1 home win?

214. Which midfielder scored the only goal in a 1-0 home win over Livingston during August 2007?

215. Which team did Queen of the South beat 4-1 away from home in the League during March 2008?

216. With which team did Queens draw 3-3 at home on the opening day of the League season, having been 3-1 up after 87 minutes?

217. Which defender did Queens sign from Celtic during January 2008?

218. How many of their 36 League games did Queens win – 14, 16 or 18?

219. True or false: this was manager Gordon Chisholm's first season in charge at the club?

220. Which striker scored 8 League goals in 32 starts this season?

CLUB HONOURS – 1

*Match up the club honour with the year/season
it was achieved*

221.	Border Cup Winners	1950/51
222.	Scottish League Challenge Cup Runners-up	1922
223.	Division Two Champions	2008/09
224.	Division Three Runners-up	2007/08
225.	Southern Counties League Winners	1997/98
226.	Scottish Qualifying Cup Winners	1992/93
227.	Division Two Champions	1924/25
228.	Southern Counties Consolation Cup Winners	1996/97
229.	UEFA Cup Second Qualification Round Entrants	2001/02
230.	Scottish Brewers Cup Winners	1923/24

BELL'S CUP (LEAGUE CHALLENGE CUP) WINNERS – 2002/03

231. Which team did The Doonhamers beat in the final?

232. What was the score in the final?

233. Can you name the Queen of the South goalscorers in the final?

234. At which stadium was the final played?

235. Which Scottish international goalkeeper played in goal for Queens in the final?

236. Which club did Queen of the South beat 5-3 away in the semi-final?

237. Following on from the previous question, which striker scored a brace in the game?

238. Which team did The Doonhamers beat 2-0 at home in the quarter-final during August 2002?

239. Which forward scored Queens' only goal in the 1-0 second round home win against Greenock Morton during August 2002?

240. What was the score when Queen of the South beat Peterhead in the first round on 6 August 2002?

POSITIONS THEY PLAYED – 2

Match up the player with his playing position

241.	Jim Doherty	Outside right
242.	Ted McMinn	Inside forward
243.	George Hamilton	Winger
244.	Dave Halliday	Goalkeeper
245.	Jackie Oakes	Striker
246.	Ernie Hannigan	Forward
247.	Andrew Barrowman	Inside forward
248.	Jimmy Bonthrone	Left winger
249.	George Farm	Right winger
250.	Walter Carlyle	Midfielder

CHAIRMEN

Match up the chairman with the year he took the position

251.	David Rae	1958
252.	William R.K. Jardine	1951
253.	Walter C. Johnston	1999
254.	James A.J. Currie	1960
255.	John Smith	2003
256.	Samuel C. Harkness	1994
257.	James S. Steel	1947
258.	Norman G. Blount	1993
259.	Ronnie Bradford	1965
260.	Matthew Fleming	1945

LEGENDS – 2

Rearrange the letters to reveal the name of a club legend

261.   ROGGEE CYOL

262.   NIA CODSKIN

263.   MYTMO BECRY

264.   ROCDWARF DYBO

265.   ORY DENNOSHER

266.   ILNE INTRAM

267.   DTE NMINCM

268.   YBLLI ONLISHOUT

269.   HIHUGE HAGCALLER

270.   MIJ STONEPART

SCOTTISH FA CUP RUNNERS-UP – 2007/08

271. Which team beat Queen of the South in the final?

272. What was the score in the final?

273. Which defender scored in the final in the 53rd minute to bring the score to 2-2?

274. At which stadium was the final played?

275. Can you name seven of the starting eleven that played for Queens in the final?

276. What was the attendance in the final – 48,821, 50,821 or 52,821?

277. Which team did Queens beat 4-3 in the semi-final during April 2008?

278. What was the score when The Doonhamers beat Dundee in the quarter-final of the competition?

279. Which team did Queen of the South beat 5-0 away from home in the third round during November 2007?

280. Following on from the previous question, can you name the two strikers that scored braces in the game?

2003/04

281. Who managed Queen of the South during this season?

282. Which midfielder signed for The Doonhamers from Inverness Caledonian Thistle during July 2003?

283. With how many points did The Doonhamers finish in 5th place in Division One?

284. Which forward scored 13 League goals during this season, finishing as the club's highest scorer?

285. Which team did The Doonhamers beat 1-0 on the last day of the League season, during May 2004?

286. Following on from the previous question, which Queens forward scored the goal?

287. Which striker scored 12 League goals in 19 starts and 7 substitute appearances for Queens during this season?

288. Which forward scored an 85th-minute winner against Brechin City in the club's 1-0 home win during December 2003?

289. How many of their 36 League matches did the club win – 13, 14 or 15?

290. Which striker scored Queens' only goal when they beat Ross County 1-0 at home during August 2003?

PLAYING YEARS AT THE CLUB – 2

Match the player with his time at the club

291.	Warren Hawke	1961-64
292.	Hughie Gallacher	2007-09
293.	Jocky Dempster	1982-84
294.	Drew Busby	1948-55
295.	Derek Townsley	1921
296.	Warren Moon	1969-79
297.	Billy Reid	2006-07
298.	Dougie McBain	1996-99
299.	Ernie Hannigan (first spell)	1999-2001
300.	Stephen Dobbie	1984-89

MANAGERS – 2

Match up the manager with the year he took charge of The Doonhamers

301.	Ian McCall	1987
302.	George McLachlan	2004
303.	Harold Davis	1978
304.	George Farm	2005
305.	Harry Hood	1970
306.	David Wilson	2007
307.	Mike Jackson	1961
308.	Willie Hunter	1935
309.	Iain Scott	1981
310.	Gordon Chisholm	1975

BOBBY BLACK

311. How many goals did Bobby score in his Doonhamers career?

312. In what position did Bobby play?

313. From which club did Bobby sign to join Queen of the South in 1952?

314. True or false: Bobby played his entire career wearing the same pair of football boots?

315. For which west of England non-League club did Bobby play after he left Queen of the South in 1961?

316. How many appearances did Bobby make for The Doonhamers – 326, 336 or 346?

317. Bobby was born in which year – 1926, 1927 or 1928?

318. Bobby made his international debut for Scottish League in a 3-1 win against Eire in Dublin in 1954, but how many of the three goals did he score?

319. With which club did Bobby win a League Cup medal in 1950?

320. True or false: Bobby attended Queens' 90th anniversary celebrations on 21 March 2009?

GEORGE FARM

321. Which honour did George win with Blackpool in 1953?

322. At which club did George start his professional career in 1947?

323. How many League appearances did George make for Queens – 109, 119 or 129?

324. Which club did George manage from 1967 to 1970, winning the Scottish Cup in 1968?

325. George was born on 13 July 1924 in which Scottish city?

326. In what position did George play?

327. From which club did George sign to join Queens in 1960?

328. On 18 October 1952 George made his international debut for Scotland in a 2-1 home win against which country?

329. Between 1952 and 1959 how many appearances did George make for Scotland – 10, 15 or 20?

330. At which club did George finish his managerial career in 1974?

WHERE DID THEY COME FROM? –1

*Match up the player with the club he left
to join Queen of the South*

331.	Eric Paton	Greenock Morton
332.	David Kinnear	Gretna
333.	Robert Connor	Clydebank
334.	David Weatherston	Carlisle United
335.	Steve Tosh	Meadowbank Thistle
336.	Ken Eadie	St Johnstone
337.	Rocco Quinn	Partick Thistle
338.	Ivor Broadis	Airdrieonians
339.	Colin Harris	Hamilton Academical
340.	Warren Hawke	Dunfermline Athletic

WHERE DID THEY GO? – 1

*Match up the player with the club he joined
on leaving Queen of the South*

341.	Derek Frye	Albion Rovers
342.	Billy McLaren (first spell)	Kello Rovers
343.	Brian Gilmour	Wrexham
344.	Davie Irons	Stranraer
345.	Andy Goram	Alloa Athletic
346.	Ted McMinn	Elgin City
347.	Alex Totten	FC Haka
348.	Bernie Slaven	Rangers
349.	Len Wootton	Raith Rovers
350.	Graham Weir	Greenock Morton

TRANSFERS

Match up the player with the transfer paid/received for his services

351.	Crawford Boyd to Hearts, 1979	£1,500
352.	George Farm from Blackpool, 1960	£25,000
353.	Freddie Jenkins to Chelsea, 1949	Free
354.	Ted McMinn to Rangers, 1984	£2,000
355.	Neil Martin from Alloa Athletic, 1961	£250,000
356.	Rocco Quinn from Hamilton Academical	£25,000
357.	Joe Dodds from Celtic, 1922	£100,000
358.	Andy Thomson to Southend United, 1994	£1,000
359.	Jackie Law from Airdrieonians, 1936	£10,000
360.	Rowan Alexander to St Mirren, 1983	£3,000

ANDY THOMSON

361. Andy was born in Motherwell on 1 April in which year – 1971, 1972 or 1973?

362. For which Kent League club did Andy sign in 1999 for £25,000?

363. Which Scottish club made a rejected offer of £150,000 for Andy in 1994?

364. How many League appearances did Andy make for The Doonhamers – 155, 165 or 175?

365. How many goals, in all competitions, did Andy score for Queens – 109, 114 or 119?

366. At which Scottish club did Andy finish his professional playing career in 2008?

367. For which club did Andy play from 2001 to 2003, making 66 League appearances and scoring 28 League goals?

368. What honour did Andy win in 1992 and again in 1994 while at Queens?

369. In what position did Andy play?

370. Besides Queens and the club in Q366, Andy has played for two other Scottish clubs. Name them.

IAIN McCHESNEY

371. In which year was Iain born – 1944, 1945 or 1946?

372. Iain joined Queen of the South in July 1960 from which club?

373. How many appearances, in all competitions, did Iain make for The Doonhamers – 585, 600 or 615?

374. Iain was awarded a testimonial in 1971, but who were the opponents?

375. Iain made his full Queens debut in 1961 in a 4-1 win against which club?

376. Following on from the previous question, Iain scored two of the four goals, but which player assisted both goals?

377. How many goals did Iain score in his Queens career – 69, 79 or 89?

378. Which manager signed Iain for Queens in 1960?

379. In what position did Iain play?

380. For how many years did Iain play for The Doonhamers?

TED McMINN

381.   Ted was born in Castle Douglas, Scotland, on 28
       September in which year – 1960, 1961 or 1962?

382.   What is Ted's real first name?

383.   Which club did Ted join in 1984 when he left Queens?

384.   In what position did Ted play?

385.   How many League appearances did Ted make for The
       Doonhamers – 68, 78 or 88?

386.   Against which club did Ted make his Queens debut, in
       a 1-1 draw on 6 November 1982?

387.   From which club did Ted join Queens in 1982 for £325?

388.   How many League goals did Ted score for The
       Doonhamers – 3, 5 or 7?

389.   Which English club did Ted join in February 1988 for
       £300,000?

390.   Ted finished his professional playing career in 1998 at
       which non-League Buckinghamshire club?

JIM PATTERSON

391. What was Jim's nickname at Queens?

392. How many League and Cup appearances did Jim make for The Doonhamers – 442, 452 or 462?

393. In what position did Jim play?

394. Jim made his Queens debut in a home match on 12 November 1949 against which club?

395. During the 1961/62 season Queen of the South beat Cowdenbeath 7-0, with Jim scoring how many goals?

396. Jim's last game for Queens was on 4 May 1963 at Shawfield Stadium, against which team?

397. How many goals did Jim score in his Doonhamers career – 231, 241 or 251?

398. How many years did Jim spend at Queens?

399. At which club did Jim spend his youth playing career before signing for Queens in 1949?

400. True or false: Jim played five times for Scotland?

WHICH TEAM ARE QUEENS PLAYING? – 1

*If Queens were playing at these grounds,
who would be the opponents?*

401. **Falkirk Stadium**

402. **Rugby Park**

403. **McDiarmid Park**

404. **Dens Park**

405. **Pittodrie Stadium**

406. **Ibrox Park**

407. **Ochilview Park**

408. **Celtic Park**

409. **Cliftonhill**

410. **Tannadice Park**

MATCH THE YEAR – 1

Match up the year with the event that took place

411. The first ever Scottish League match
     under floodlights was played between
     Rangers and Queen of the South   1933

412. Queen of the South were Scottish Cup
     runners-up to Rangers   1991

413. Queens won the Potts Cup for
     the first time   2008

414. John Connolly became Second Division
     Manager of the Season   1947

415. Queens won the Algiers invitational
     tournament   1999

416. Ally McLeod became manager of Queens   1936

417. The first Queen of the South match-day
     programme was published   1974

418. The lowest recorded attendance of
     300 saw Queens beat Alloa Athletic 1-0   2002

419. Freddie Jenkins joined The Doonhamers   1921

420. Scenes for the film A Shot at Glory
     were shot at Palmerston Park   1956

JAMES 'JIM' THOMSON

421. Jim was born in Stirling on 15 May in which year – 1971, 1972 or 1973?

422. At which club did Jim start his professional career in 1991, playing 151 League matches scoring 11 League goals?

423. What is Jim's nickname?

424. Jim's first spell at Queens was from 1997 to 1999, but from which club did he sign?

425. In what position does Jim play?

426. Jim made his 300th appearance for Queens on 20 October 2007 in a First Division match against which opponents?

427. How many League appearances did Jim make in his first spell at Queens – 45, 50 or 55?

428. Jim re-joined The Doonhamers for his second spell in 2001, but for which club did he play in between his two Queens spells?

429. Jim scored his first Queens goal on 12 October 2002 in a 2-1 away defeat to which club?

430. Jim's first ever sending-off with Queens was on 20 December 1997 in a Second Division 2-1 home win against which opponents?

MATCH THE YEAR – 2

Match the year with the event that took place

431. Queens reached the Scottish Challenge
     Cup final for the first time   1945

432. Goalkeeper Jimmy Coupland
     signed for Queens   2007

433. Steve Tosh was born   1924

434. Robert Harris joined The Doonhamers   1933

435. Bernie Slaven played just two games
     for Queens   1902

436. John O'Neill was awarded the Second
     Division Player of the Season   1983

437. Ian Dickson was born   1973

438. Willie Fotheringham signed for
     The Doonhamers   2002

439. Billy Houliston signed for Queens   1978

440. David McNiven was born   1997

QUEENS V. STRANRAER

441. In which year did the sides first meet in a competitive competition – 1922, 1923 or 1924?

442. Following on from the previous question, what was the score in the game – 8-0 to Queen of the South, 4-4 draw or 8-0 to Stranraer?

443. In which competition did the sides met during the 2006/07 season?

444. Which midfielder scored Queens' equalizer in a 2-2 away draw in Division Two during September 2001?

445. True or false: the sides did not meet in any competition during the 1940s?

446. What was the score when Queen of the South beat Stranraer in the Scottish FA Cup first round during January 1932?

447. Which midfielder scored the only goal for Queens in a 1-0 home League win during March 2006?

448. True or false: Queens beat Stranraer 6-4 away from home in the Scottish FA Cup third round during February 1985?

449. What was the score when the sides met at Stranraer during the 1973/74 League season – 3-3, 4-4 or 5-5?

450. Which forward scored a brace in a 4-3 away win over Stranraer in Division Two during December 1997?

HAT-TRICKS

Match up the player with the number of hat-tricks scored for The Doonhamers

451.	**Jackie Brown**	*3*
452.	**Ian Reid**	*4*
453.	**Jim Patterson**	*3*
454.	**Lex Law**	*5*
455.	**Tommy Bryce (Mark 2)**	*3*
456.	**Rowan Alexander**	*2*
457.	**Jimmy Robertson**	*11*
458.	**Bobby Black**	*1*
459.	**Willie Dougan**	*2*
460.	**Billy Houliston**	*4*

CLUB HONOURS – 2

*Match up the club honour with the year/season
it was achieved*

461. **Division 2 Runners-up**   *1936*

462. **Western League Champions**   *1961*

463. **B&Q Cup Semi-Finalists**   *2006/07*

464. **Bell's Cup (League Challenge Cup) Winners**   *1939/40*

465. **Southern Counties League Cup Winners**   *1922/23*

466. **Algiers Invitational Tournament Winners**   *1991/92*

467. **Scottish Brewers Cup Winners**   *2002/03*

468. **Scottish League South and West
      Runners-up (Wartime League)**   *1985/86*

469. **Border Cup Winners**   *1996/97*

470. **Potts Cup Winners**   *1991/92*

2006/07

471. Which team did The Doonhamers beat 4-3 at home during January 2007?

472. Following on from the previous question, which Queens player scored a brace in the game?

473. True or false: Queen of the South failed to win any of their first ten League matches?

474. Who managed The Doonhamers this season?

475. How many of their 36 League matches did The Doonhamers win – 9, 10 or 11?

476. Can you name either of the Queens players that finished as the club's highest scorers with eight goals each?

477. Which defender signed for The Doonhamers from Gretna during January 2007?

478. From which club did Jim Lauchlan sign when he joined Queen of the South during August 2006?

479. Which team did Queens beat 3-0 away during February 2007, with Stephen Dobbie scoring a brace in the game?

480. Which midfielder scored a brace in a 2-0 home win against Dundee during November 2006?

LEAGUE POSITIONS – 3

Match up the season with the club's finishing position in the League

481.	1988/89	13th in Division Two
482.	1987/88	7th in Division Two
483.	1986/87	8th in Division Two
484.	1985/86	14th in Division One
485.	1984/85	2nd in Division Two
486.	1983/84	14th in Division One
487.	1982/83	2nd in Division Two
488.	1981/82	6th in Division Two
489.	1980/81	10th in Division One
490.	1979/80	7th in Division One

CAPPED QUEENS

*Match up the player with caps/year achieved
while playing for Queens*

491. Lex Law

1 Scottish Under-15 cap
in 1997

492. Peter Dickson

1 Scottish Army cap
in 1945

493. Billy Houliston

3 Scottish Under-21 caps
in 1997 and 1999

494. Ian Mitchell

1 Scottish Under-23 cap
in 1976

495. Chris Doig

1 Scottish cap in 1953

496. Keith Houliston

1 Scottish Under-23 cap
in 1956

497. Murray Landsborough

3 Full Scottish caps
in 1948 and 1949

498. Thomas Baxter

2 Scottish Under-18 caps
in 1965

499. David Mathieson

3 Scottish Amateur caps
in 1970 and 1971

500. Jim Patterson

1 Scottish Under-21 cap
in 1979

SCOTTISH LEAGUE CHALLENGE CUP RUNNERS-UP – 1997/98

501.   Which team beat Queen of the South 1-0 in the final?

502.   At which stadium was the final played?

503.   Can you name seven of the starting eleven that played for Queens in the final?

504.   Which team did Queens beat 2-0 away in the semi-final during September 1997?

505.   Following on from the previous question, can you name Queens' goalscorers in the game?

506.   Which forward scored a brace in a 3-2 home win against Airdrie in the third round of the competition?

507.   Which team did the Doonhamers beat 2-0 in the first round of the competition?

508.   Following on from the previous question, what was the score in the game – 2-0, 2-1 or 3-1?

509.   Which team did Queen of the South beat 2-0 at home in the second round of the competition?

510.   Following on from the previous question, can you name the Queens striker that scored both goals in the game?

QUEENS V. ABERDEEN

511. True or false: the sides did not meet in competitive competition during the 1990s?

512. What was the score when the sides met in the Scottish FA Cup semi-final during April 2008?

513. Following on from the previous question, can you name two of Queens' goalscorers?

514. In which year did the sides first meet in Division One – 1932, 1933 or 1934?

515. In which competition did the sides meet during the 2002/03 season?

516. What was the score when Queens visited Aberdeen for a League Cup tie during the 1951/52 season – 5-4 to Aberdeen, 4-4 draw or 5-4 to Queen of the South?

517. Which Queens player joined Aberdeen in 1938, signed by former Queens player Dave Halliday?

518. True or false: the sides did not meet in competitive competition during the 1980s?

519. Which forward scored for Queens in their 2-1 home defeat to Aberdeen in the League Cup second round during September 2001?

520. In which year did the sides first meet in the Scottish FA Cup – 1937, 1938 or 1939?

WHERE DID THEY COME FROM? – 2

*Match up the player with the club he left
to join Queen of the South*

521.	Allan Preston	Clyde
522.	George Farm	Falkirk
523.	Sean O'Connor	St Johnstone
524.	Stewart Kean	East Fife
525.	Bobby Black	Carlisle United
526.	Bobby Shearer	St Mirren
527.	Neil Scally	Barnsley
528.	Phil Watson	Annan Athletic
529.	Gary Arbuckle	Rangers
530.	Ernie Bond	Blackpool

WHERE DID THEY GO? – 2

Match up the player with the club he joined on leaving Queen of the South

531.	Stephen Grindlay	Dumbarton
532.	Andy Aitken (first spell)	Kilmarnock
533.	Steven Bell	Ayr United
534.	Sandy Hodge (first spell)	Carlisle United
535.	Shaun Dillon	Stranraer
536.	Tommy Lang	Gretna
537.	Willie Gibson	Stenhousemuir
538.	Bob McDermid	Ipswich Town
539.	Derek Allan	Stirling Albion
540.	Jimmy Brown	Aberdeen

WHICH TEAM ARE QUEENS PLAYING? – 2

If Queens were playing at these grounds,
who would be the opponents?

541. **Balmoor**

542. **Stark's Park**

543. **St Mirren Park**

544. **East End Park**

545. **Fir Park**

546. **New Douglas Park**

547. **Excelsior Stadium**

548. **Tynecastle Stadium**

549. **Easter Road**

550. **Stair Park**

LEAGUE GOALSCORERS - 1

Match up the player with the number of
League goals scored for Queens

551.	Neil Martin	17
552.	Andy Thomson	5
553.	Iain McChesney	8
554.	Paddy Atkinson	93
555.	Billy Reid	78
556.	Stephen Dobbie	33
557.	Ken Eadie	22
558.	Jocky Dempster	10
559.	Sam English	47
560.	Willie McLean	67

DAVE HALLIDAY

561.   True or false: in 1924 Dave's younger brother Billy joined Queen of the South?

562.   Dave was born in Dumfries on 11 December in which year – 1900, 1901 or 1902?

563.   Dave made 19 League appearances for The Doonhamers in 1920, scoring how many League goals – 5, 9 or 13?

564.   Dave was manager of which English club from 1955 to 1958?

565.   When Dave left Queen of the South in 1920 which Scottish club did he join?

566.   In 1925 which north-east club signed Dave for £4,000?

567.   Dave made 488 career League and Cup appearances, scoring how many goals – 173, 273 or 373?

568.   In what position did Dave play at Queens?

569.   At which non-League Somerset club was Dave a player/manager in the 1936/37 season?

570.   Which ex-Queens player did Dave sign when he was manager of Aberdeen in 1938?

PAUL BURNS

571.   In what year did Paul join Queen of the South?

572.   In what position does Paul play?

573.   Paul scored his first goal for Queens in a 3-0 League Cup victory on 23 September 2003, against which opponents?

574.   Paul was born in Irvine on 18 May in which year – 1984, 1985 or 1986?

575.   Paul made his Queens debut against Arbroath on 18 March 2003, coming on in the 84th minute as a substitute for which player?

576.   Against which club did Paul make his 200th appearance for The Doonhamers in the Challenge Cup on 18 August 2009?

577.   How many League appearances did Paul make in the 2007/08 season, scoring five goals?

578.   True or false: Paul was the first footballer in the United Kingdom to contract swine flu?

579.   How many of the goals did Paul score in the 4-3 victory over Aberdeen in the semi-final of the 2008 Scottish Cup?

580.   What is Paul's nickname?

ANDY AITKEN

581.   What is Andy's middle name – Richard, Robert or Roy?

582.   When Andy joined Queens in 1996 for his first spell, who was the chairman of the club?

583.   Which club did Andy join in 2004 when he left Queens?

584.   In Andy's two spells at Queens how many League appearances did he make – 240, 250 or 260?

585.   Which club did Andy join in 2009?

586.   Andy was born in Dumfries on 2 February in which year – 1978, 1979 or 1980?

587.   In what position did Andy play at Queens?

588.   Which Queens manager re-signed Andy in 2006?

589.   How many League goals did Andy score in his two spells at Queens – 4, 8 or 12?

590.   At which club did Andy start his professional playing career?

ALAN DAVIDSON

591. Alan was born in Airdrie on 17 April in which year – 1960, 1962 or 1964?

592. How many appearances in all competitions did Alan make for Queens – 264, 364 or 464?

593. From which club did Alan sign for The Doonhamers in 1982?

594. For which Australian club did Alan play in 1988/89?

595. In what position did Alan play?

596. At which club did Alan start his professional playing career in 1979?

597. How many goals did Alan score for Queens?

598. How many spells as a player did Alan have at Queen of the South?

599. For which club did Alan play between 1994 and 1997, where he made only 22 League appearances?

600. How many League games did Alan play for The Doonhamers – 312, 322 or 332?

PLAYER OF THE YEAR – 2

Match up the player with the year he won the award

601.	Jim Thomson	1984
602.	Stuart Gordon	1974
603.	Billy Reid	1968
604.	Crawford Boyd	2005
605.	Mike Jackson	1995
606.	Steve Bowey	1988
607.	Nobby Clark	1991
608.	Alan Davidson	1970
609.	Tommy Bryce (Mark 2)	1978
610.	Iain McChesney	2003

QUEENS V. CELTIC

611. In which year did the sides first meet, in the Scottish FA Cup, ending in a 0-0 home draw?

612. True or false: the clubs have not met in the League since the 1963/64 season?

613. What was the score when Queen of the South visited Celtic during the 1962/63 League season?

614. How many of the four League and two League Cup meetings during the 1960s did Queens win against Celtic?

615. In which competition did the sides meet during August 1989?

616. What was the score when Queen of the South beat Celtic at home during the 1956/57 season?

617. True or false: Queen of the South beat Celtic in the clubs' first League meeting of the 1933/34 season?

618. What was the score between the sides in the Scottish League Cup quarter-final during September 1990?

619. Which team finished higher in Division One during the 1956/57 season?

620. True or false: Queens beat Celtic both at home and away during the 1957/58 season?

2004/05

621. Queens recorded their first League win, 3-1 away, in their second match of the season against which team, with David McNiven scoring a brace?

622. How many of their 36 League matches did Queens win – 12, 13 or 14?

623. Which goalkeeper signed from Aldershot Town during November 2004?

624. Which striker finished the season with 7 goals in 22 starts and 1 substitute appearance?

625. True or false: The Doonhamers lost their first three home League matches?

626. Which forward scored a 90th-minute winner, his only ever Queens League goal, against Partick Thistle in a 2-1 away win during September 2004?

627. Which midfielder scored Queens' only goal in a 1-0 home win in the League during November 2004 against Airdrie United?

628. Which team did Queens beat 2-1 away on the last day of the League season, with forward David McNiven scoring the winner after 87 minutes?

629. David McNiven finished as the club's highest scorer this season, with how many goals?

630. Which Australian midfielder signed for Queens from Livingston during February 2005?

WHICH TEAM ARE QUEENS PLAYING? – 3

*If Queens were playing at these grounds,
who would be the opponents?*

631.   Station Park

632.   Glebe Park

633.   Gayfield Park

634.   Links Park

635.   Hampden Park

636.   Cappielow Park

637.   Broadwood Stadium

638.   Strathclyde Homes Stadium

639.   Bayview Stadium

640.   Somerset Park

LEAGUE GOALSCORERS – 2

Match up the player with the number of League goals scored for Queens

641.	Darren Henderson	58
642.	Rowan Alexander	3
643.	Sandy Hodge	38
644.	Steve Bowey	71
645.	Alex Burke	2
646.	John O'Neill	16
647.	Ian Cochrane	33
648.	Emilio Jaconelli	9
649.	Sean O'Connor	1
650.	Peter Weatherson	13

HUGHIE GALLACHER

651. Hughie was born in Bellshill, North Lanarkshire on 2 February in which year – 1903, 1905 or 1907?

652. How many goals did Hughie score for Queens – 15, 17 or 19?

653. What was Hughie's middle name – Keenan, Kilpatrick or Kelso?

654. From 1924 to 1935 Hughie made 20 international appearances for Scotland, scoring how many goals?

655. Hughie made his Queens debut on 29 January 1921 in a 7-0 win against St Cuthbert Wanderers, scoring how many of the seven goals?

656. In what position did Hughie play?

657. When Hughie left Queens in 1921 he moved to which club, making 111 League appearances and scoring 91 League goals?

658. In his entire professional career how many goals did Hughie score – 263, 363 or 463?

659. At which north-east club did Hughie finish his playing career in 1939?

660. Which club signed Hughie in December 1925 for £6,500?

NEIL MARTIN

661. From which club did Neil sign to play for Queens in 1961?

662. Neil made his debut at international level for Scotland on 9 November 1965 in a 1-0 home win against which country?

663. How many League appearances did Neil make for The Doonhamers – 61, 71 or 81?

664. Neil was born in Tranent, East Lothian, on 20 October in which wartime year?

665. Which team in 1963 paid £7,500 for Neil?

666. How many full international appearances did Neil make for Scotland?

667. In what position did Neil play?

668. Which north-east club paid £45,000 to sign Neil in 1965?

669. True or false: Neil scored over 100 League goals in both the Scottish and English Leagues?

670. At which Irish club did Neil finish his professional career in 1978?

ROWAN ALEXANDER

671. What is Rowan's middle name – Samuel, Steven or Sidney?

672. Rowan succeeded which Queens manager in 1996?

673. At which club did Rowan finish his professional playing career in 2003?

674. When Rowan joined Queens for his second spell in 1995 from which club did he sign?

675. In what position did Rowan play?

676. With whom did Rowan co-manage the club from 1996 to 1999?

677. In Rowan's two spells at Queens how many League appearances did he make – 144, 154 or 164?

678. Which Scottish club did Rowan manage from 2000 to 2007?

679. Which is the only English club that Rowan played for during his career?

680. True or false: Rowan won the Scottish Football League 1, 2 and 3 Championships as a manager?

JOHN 'JOCKY' DEMPSTER

681. In what position did Jocky play?

682. How many goals in all competitions did Jocky score for The Doonhamers – 88, 98 or 108?

683. For which club did Jocky play when he left Queens in 1979?

684. Where in Scotland was Jocky born?

685. How many appearances in all competition did Jocky make for Queens – 315, 335 or 355?

686. Alongside which three Queens teammates did Jocky mostly play?

687. At which club did Jocky finish his professional playing career in 1981?

688. In which year was Jocky born – 1944, 1946 or 1948?

689. When Jocky made his Queens debut in 1969 he scored twice against which club?

690. Which member of the board of directors actually signed Jocky in 1969?

WHO AM I?

691. I signed for Queen of the South in 1936 from Wolverhampton Wanderers.

692. I was born in Dumfries in 1902 and after playing for Queens I went on to play for Aston Villa and Middlesborough.

693. I am a goalkeeper and signed for Queens in July 1946.

694. I signed for Queens from Motherwell Juniors in 1932 and played in the 1936 Algiers invitational tournament.

695. In 2009 I was signed as an emergency loan from St Mirren and scored on my Queens debut against Dunfermline Athletic.

696. I had two spells with The Doonhamers, the first in 1921 and again in 1933.

697. I made a total of 321 first-team appearances while playing as a defender for Queens from 1972 to 1982.

698. I signed in August 2009 and I am a defensive midfielder.

699. I played for Queens, Berwick Rangers and Third Lanark in my career and was capped three times for Scotland.

700. I spent 13 years at Queens and I was called up to play for Scotland in 1952 v. The Army in Newcastle.

LEAGUE POSITIONS – 4

Match up the season with the club's finishing position in the League

701.   1978/79   3rd in Division Two

702.   1977/78   11th in Division Two

703.   1976/77   10th in Division One

704.   1975/76   7th in Division Two

705.   1974/75   11th in Division Two

706.   1973/74   12th in Division One

707.   1972/73   14th in Division One

708.   1971/72   4th in Division Two

709.   1970/71   9th in Division One

710.   1969/70   2nd in Division Two

CLUB HONOURS – 3

*Match up the club honour with the year/season
it was achieved*

711.	B.P. Youth Cup Runners-Up	1987
712.	Scottish Cup Semi-Finalists	2007/08
713.	Southern Counties Charity Cup Winners	2004
714.	Southern Counties Cup Winners	1960/61
715.	Scottish Brewers Cup Winners	1980/81
716.	Scottish Cup Runners-Up	1949/50
717.	Scottish League Cup Semi-Finalists	1985/86
718.	Southern Counties Cup Winners	1937
719.	Division 2 Runners-up	2001/02
720.	Scottish League Cup Semi-Finalists	1950/51

2005/06

721. With which team did Queens share a 0-0 home draw on Boxing Day 2005?

722. True or false: The Doonhamers failed to win any of their first four matches?

723. In which position did Queens finish in Division One – 7th, 8th or 9th?

724. Which defender did The Doonhamers sign from Gretna during January 2006?

725. John O'Neil finished as the club's highest scorer of the League season, with how many League goals?

726. True or false: Queens were unbeaten in the League during February 2006?

727. Which forward scored the winning goal when Queens beat Dundee 3-2 away during February 2006?

728. Which team did Queen of the South beat 3-2 at home in the League during April 2006?

729. Which forward did Queens sign from Hearts during January 2006?

730. How many of their 36 League matches did the club win – 7, 17 or 27?

WHICH TEAM ARE QUEENS PLAYING? – 4

*If Queens were playing at these grounds,
who would be the opponents?*

731. **Caledonian Stadium**

732. **Firhill Stadium**

733. **Almondvale Stadium**

734. **Forthbank Stadium**

735. **Recreation Park**

736. **Central Park**

737. **Victoria Park**

738. **Galabank**

739. **Shielfield Park**

740. **Borough Briggs**

TOMMY BRYCE (MARK 2)

741.   Tommy was born in Johnstone on 27 January in which year – 1960, 1962 or 1964?

742.   At which club did Tommy start his professional playing career in 1980?

743.   How many first-team games did Tommy play in his Queens career – 277, 287 or 297?

744.   Which honour did Tommy win in 1997?

745.   Tommy had three separate spells with The Doonhamers, scoring how many goals in total – 75, 85 or 95?

746.   Tommy managed which club for the 1998/99 season?

747.   In what position did Tommy play?

748.   At which club did Tommy finish his professional playing career in 2001?

749.   Which Queens manager signed Tommy in 1985?

750.   Tommy also played for two other Scottish clubs, with two spells at each. Can you name them?

GEORGE HAMILTON

751. George was born in Irvine on 7 December in which year – 1915, 1917 or 1919?

752. In what position did George play?

753. For which junior club did George play from 1934 to 1937?

754. How many League appearances did George make for The Doonhamers – 31, 41 or 51?

755. Which club did George sign for in 1938 for £3,000?

756. George made how many appearances at international level for Scotland, scoring four goals?

757. How many League goals did George score in his Queens career?

758. Against which country did George score a hat-trick away on 20 May 1951?

759. At which club did George finish his professional playing career in 1955?

760. Which former Queen of the South player signed George to play for Aberdeen?

JIMMY ROBERTSON

761.   In which year was Jimmy born – 1955, 1957 or 1959?

762.   How many League appearances did Jimmy make for Queens – 322, 332 or 342?

763.   Against which club did Jimmy make his Queens debut in November 1979, in a 2-1 away defeat?

764.   At which club did Jimmy start his professional playing career in 1977?

765.   In what position did Jimmy play?

766.   How many League goals did Jimmy score for Queens – 57, 67 or 77?

767.   Jimmy had two spells at Queens, playing for which two other clubs in between?

768.   For which youth club did Jimmy play?

769.   How many first-team appearances in all competitions did Jimmy make for The Doonhamers 400, 425 or 450?

770.   Which club did Jimmy leave to join Queens in 1979?

LEAGUE GOALSCORERS – 3

*Match up the player with the number of
League goals scored for Queens*

771.	Murray Henderson	9
772.	Tommy O'Hara	1
773.	Neil MacFarlane	4
774.	Drew Busby	2
775.	Mick Oliver	6
776.	Colin Harris	2
777.	Harry Hood	1
778.	Alex Totten	9
779	Frank McGarvey	4
780.	Tommy McCulloch	11

LEAGUE POSITIONS – 5

Match up the season with club's finishing position in the League

781. 1968/69   17th in Division One

782. 1967/68   3rd in Division Two

783. 1966/67   2nd in Division Two

784. 1965/66   5th in Division Two

785. 1964/65   5th in Division Two

786. 1963/64   3rd in Division Two

787. 1962/63   9th in Division Two

788. 1961/62   3rd in Division Two

789. 1960/61   6th in Division Two

790. 1959/60   15th in Division One

PLAYER OF THE YEAR – 3

Match up the player with the year he won the award

791.	Jim Kerr	1985
792.	Allan Ball	1989
793.	Billy Sim	1996
794.	Jimmy Robertson	1964
795.	Gary Fraser	2002
796.	Steve Mallan	1965
797.	Alan Gray	1966
798.	George Cloy	2000
799.	David Kennedy	1987
800.	Billy Collings	1980

ANSWERS

CLUB HISTORY

1.   1919
2.   Jimmy Gray
3.   UEFA Cup (second qualification round)
4.   1924/25
5.   The Doonhamers (also Queens)
6.   A Lore Burne (meaning 'to the muddy stream')
7.   1921
8.   Iain McChesney
9.   Rangers
10.   Dougie the Doonhamer

ALLAN BALL

11.   Goalkeeper
12.   Bally
13.   731
14.   True
15.   1963
16.   George Farm
17.   Falkirk
18.   True
19.   Gretna
20.   Carlisle United (1971) and Manchester City (1984)

MANAGERS – 1

21.	Billy McLaren	1993
22.	Derek Frye	1992
23.	Mike Jackson	1986
24.	Willie Ferguson	1937
25.	George Herd	1980
26.	Billy Little	1979
27.	John Connolly	2000

28.	Ally McLeod	1991
29.	Willie McLean	1973
30.	Jackie Husband	1967

GORDON CHISHOLM

31. 1960
32. Central defender
33. Hibernian
34. Dundee United
35. Ian McCall
36. 4th
37. David Rae
38. True: against Livingston in the Scottish First Division during August 2007, his first five competitive matches finishing in 1 draw and 4 defeats
39. Dundee
40. 5th

2009/10

41. 4th
42. Partick Thistle
43. Derek Holmes, Paul Burns and Willie McLaren
44. Derek Holmes
45. True: a 1-1 home draw with Dundee on 23 January 2010
46. 3-0 to Queens
47. Rocco Quinn
48. 15
49. True: 2 draws and 2 wins
50. Paul Burns

LEGENDS – 1

51. Andy Thomson

52.	Willie Savage
53.	Jackie Oakes
54.	George Hamilton
55.	Dave Halliday
56.	George Farm
57.	Bobby Black
58.	Ivor Broadis
59.	Nobby Clark
60.	Jimmy Binning

PLAYER OF THE YEAR – 1

61.	Steve Bowey	2004
62.	Allan Ball	1976
63.	Andy Thomson	1994
64.	Peter Weatherson	2001
65.	Derek Townsley	1999
66.	Crawford Boyd	1979
67.	David Mathieson	1997
68.	Jimmy Robertson	1992
69.	Bobby Parker	1986
70.	Tommy O'Hara	1977

LEAGUE POSITIONS – 1

71.	2008/09	5th in Division One
72.	2007/08	4th in Division One
73.	2006/07	8th in Division One
74.	2005/06	8th in Division One
75.	2004/05	4th in Division One
76.	2003/04	5th in Division One
77.	2002/03	5th in Division One
78.	2001/02	1st in Division Two
79.	2000/01	6th in Division Two

80.   1999/2000   9th in Division Two

2008/09

81.   7-1 to Queen of the South
82.   Stephen Dobbie
83.   Steve Tosh
84.   Stephen Dobbie
85.   Barry Wilson
86.   St Johnstone
87.   Gordon Chisholm
88.   12
89.   Stewart Kean
90.   Stephen Dobbie and David Weatherston

UEFA CUP – AUGUST 2008

91.   Nordsjaelland
92.   2-1 to Nordsjaelland
93.   Danish
94.   4,406
95.   Sean O'Connor
96.   Robert Harris
97.   2-1 to Nordsjaelland
98.   Jamie Adams
99.   France
100.   Farum Park stadium

CLUB RECORDS

101.   Dundee
102.   26,552
103.   £250,000
104.   2003/04
105.   67

106.	Jimmy Rutherford
107.	John Connolly
108.	Stranraer
109.	55
110.	Jim Patterson

DIVISION TWO CHAMPIONS – 2001/02

111.	John Connolly
112.	8 points (Queen of the South, 67 points, and Alloa, 59 points)
113.	John O'Neil
114.	Greenock Morton
115.	Berwick Rangers
116.	True: 2 draws and 1 defeat
117.	Greenock Morton
118.	Peter Weatherson
119.	Derek Anderson
120.	20

QUEENS V. RANGERS

121.	Robert Harris
122.	Rangers (5-1 at home and 4-0 away at Palmerston Park)
123.	True
124.	8-1 to Rangers (Rangers won 4-0 at home and 4-1 at Palmerston Park)
125.	True
126.	7-0 to Rangers
127.	False: Queens beat them 2-1 at home but lost 2-0 away
128.	25 years (last met August 1983)
129.	1-1
130.	True

2002/03

131.	*Colin Scott, Andy Goram and Jamie Campbell*
132.	*St Johnstone*
133.	*Derek Lyle*
134.	*Steve Bowey*
135.	*Peter Weatherson*
136.	*Brian McLaughlin*
137.	*Clyde*
138.	*False: won 2 and lost 1*
139.	*12*
140.	*John O'Neil*

IVOR BROADIS

141.	*Arthur*
142.	*8*
143.	*True*
144.	*Inside forward*
145.	*1922*
146.	*63*
147.	*Carlisle United*
148.	*20*
149.	*Ivan*
150.	*Football journalist*

JIMMY BINNING

151.	*1927*
152.	*East Fife*
153.	*288*
154.	*Left back*
155.	*Arbroath*
156.	*True*
157.	*Jimmy McKinnell Junior*

158.   English League
159.   6
160.   10th

POSITIONS THEY PLAYED – 1

161.   Billy Halliday   Inside left
162.   Graeme Robertson   Fullback
163.   Andy Goram   Goalkeeper
164.   Chris Balderstone   Centre back/Midfielder
165.   David Craig   Defender
166.   Willie Telfer   Centre half
167.   Bobby Shearer   Right back
168.   Jimmy Brown   Centre forward
169.   Billy Findlay   Midfielder
170.   Ken Eadie   Striker

PLAYING YEARS AT THE CLUB – 1

171.   Willie Telfer   1960-61
172.   Andy Aitken (first spell)   1996-2004
173.   Billy Houliston   1945-52
174.   Tommy Bryce (second spell)   1994-98
175.   Willie Gibson   2001-07
176.   Jimmy Brown   1949-50
177.   Jimmy Robertson (first spell)   1980-87
178.   Jim Patterson   1949-63
179.   Iain McChesney   1960-81
180.   George Hamilton   1937-38

TOP APPEARANCES

181.   Jim Kerr   403
182.   Iain McChesney   615
183.   Willie Savage   369

184.	Dougie Sharpe	431
185.	Allan Ball	731
186.	Alan Davidson	364
187.	Roy Henderson	381
188.	Jim Patterson	462
189.	Jimmy Robertson	400
190.	Jackie Oakes	457

QUEENS V. GREENOCK MORTON

191. Derek Holmes
192. 3 (1-1 at home and 2-2 and 0-0 away)
193. Stephen Dobbie
194. True: Morton beat Queens 5-2 and 2-0 at home and 2-0 and 3-2 at Palmerston Park
195. 2-1 to Queen of the South
196. 3
197. Peter Weatherson
198. False: they met during 1949/50, 1951/52 and 1959/60
199. 1927/28
200. Scottish League Challenge Cup

LEAGUE POSITIONS – 2

201.	1998/99	4th in Division Two
202.	1997/98	4th in Division Two
203.	1996/97	5th in Division Two
204.	1995/96	7th in Division Two
205.	1994/95	7th in Division Two
206.	1993/94	5th in Division Two
207.	1992/93	10th in Division Two
208.	1991/92	11th in Division Two
209.	1990/91	12th in Division Two
210.	1989/90	10th in Division Two

2007/08

211.   16

212.   Brian Gilmour

213.   Dundee

214.   Neil Scally

215.   Clyde

216.   St Johnstone

217.   Craig Reid

218.   14

219.   True

220.   Sean O'Connor

CLUB HONOURS – 1

221.	Border Cup Winners	1992/93
222.	Scottish League Challenge Cup Runners-up	1997/98
223.	Division Two Champions	2001/02
224.	Division Three Runners-up	1924/25
225.	Southern Counties League Winners	1996/97
226.	Scottish Qualifying Cup Winners	1923/24
227.	Division Two Champions	1950/51
228.	Southern Counties Consolation Cup Winners	1922
229.	UEFA Cup Second Qualification Round Entrants	2008/09
230.	Scottish Brewers Cup Winners	2007/08

BELL'S CUP (LEAGUE CHALLENGE CUP) WINNERS – 2002/03

231.   Brechin City

232.   2-0 to Queen of the South

233.   John O'Neil and Derek Lyle

234.   Broadwood Stadium (Clyde's home ground)

235.   Andy Goram

236.   St Mirren

237.   Paul Shields

238. Dumbarton

239. Sean O'Connor

240. 2-0

POSITIONS THEY PLAYED – 2

241.	Jim Doherty	Midfielder
242.	Ted McMinn	Winger
243.	George Hamilton	Inside forward
244.	Dave Halliday	Forward
245.	Jackie Oakes	Left winger
246.	Ernie Hannigan	Outside right
247.	Andrew Barrowman	Striker
248.	Jimmy Bonthrone	Inside forward
249.	George Farm	Goalkeeper
250.	Walter Carlyle	Right winger

CHAIRMEN

251.	David Rae	2003
252.	William R.K. Jardine	1993
253.	Walter C. Johnston	1947
254.	James A.J. Currie	1958
255.	John Smith	1945
256.	Samuel C. Harkness	1965
257.	James S. Steel	1951
258.	Norman G. Blount	1994
259.	Ronnie Bradford	1999
260.	Matthew Fleming	1960

LEGENDS – 2

261. George Cloy

262. Ian Dickson

263. Tommy Bryce (Mark 2)

264.   *Crawford Boyd*

265.   *Roy Henderson*

266.   *Neil Martin*

267.   *Ted McMinn*

268.   *Billy Houliston*

269.   *Hughie Gallacher*

270.   *Jim Patterson*

SCOTTISH FA CUP RUNNERS-UP – 2007/08

271.   *Rangers*

272.   *3-2 to Rangers*

273.   *Jim Thomson*

274.   *Hampden Park, Glasgow*

275.   *Jamie MacDonald, Ryan McCann, Jim Thomson, Andy Aitken, Robert Harris, Jamie McQuilken, Neil MacFarlane, Steve Tosh, Paul Burns, Stephen Dobbie and Sean O'Connor*

276.   *48,821*

277.   *Aberdeen*

278.   *2-0 to Queen of the South*

279.   *Peterhead*

280.   *Stephen Dobbie and Sean O'Connor*

2003/04

281.   *John Connolly*

282.   *David Bagan*

283.   *54 points*

284.   *Alex Burke*

285.   *Falkirk*

286.   *Emilio Jaconelli*

287.   *Sean O'Connor*

288.   *Garry Wood*

289.   *15*

290.   Derek Lyle

PLAYING YEARS AT THE CLUB – 2

291.	Warren Hawke	1999-2001
292.	Hughie Gallacher	1921
293.	Jocky Dempster	1969-79
294.	Drew Busby	1982-84
295.	Derek Townsley	1996-99
296.	Warren Moon	2006-07
297.	Billy Reid	1984-89
298.	Dougie McBain	1948-55
299.	Ernie Hannigan (first spell)	1961-64
300.	Stephen Dobbie	2007-09

MANAGERS – 2

301.	Ian McCall	2005
302.	George McLachlan	1935
303.	Harold Davis	1970
304.	George Farm	1961
305.	Harry Hood	1981
306.	David Wilson	1987
307.	Mike Jackson	1975
308.	Willie Hunter	1978
309.	Iain Scott	2004
310.	Gordon Chisholm	2007

BOBBY BLACK

311.	120
312.	Outside right
313.	East Fife
314.	True
315.	Bath City

316.	346
317.	1927
318.	2
319.	East Fife
320.	True

GEORGE FARM

321.	The FA Cup
322.	Hibernian
323.	119
324.	Dunfermline Athletic
325.	Edinburgh
326.	Goalkeeper
327.	Blackpool
328.	Wales
329.	10
330.	Raith Rovers

WHERE DID THEY COME FROM? – 1

331.	Eric Paton	Clydebank
332.	David Kinnear	Dunfermline Athletic
333.	Robert Connor	Partick Thistle
334.	David Weatherston	St Johnstone
335.	Steve Tosh	Gretna
336.	Ken Eadie	Airdrieonians
337.	Rocco Quinn	Hamilton Academical
338.	Ivor Broadis	Carlisle United
339.	Colin Harris	Meadowbank Thistle
340.	Warren Hawke	Greenock Morton

WHERE DID THEY GO? – 1

| 341. | Derek Frye | Stranraer |

342.	Billy McLaren (first spell)	Greenock Morton
343.	Brian Gilmour	FC Haka
344.	Davie Irons	Kello Rovers
345.	Andy Goram	Elgin City
346.	Ted McMinn	Rangers
347.	Alex Totten	Alloa Athletic
348.	Bernie Slaven	Albion Rovers
349.	Len Wootton	Wrexham
350.	Graham Weir	Raith Rovers

TRANSFERS

351.	Crawford Boyd to Hearts, 1979	£25,000
352.	George Farm from Blackpool, 1960	£3,000
353.	Freddie Jenkins to Chelsea, 1949	£10,000
354.	Ted McMinn to Rangers, 1984	£100,000
355.	Neil Martin from Alloa Athletic, 1961	£2,000
356.	Rocco Quinn from Hamilton Academical	Free
357.	Joe Dodds from Celtic, 1922	£1,000
358.	Andy Thomson to Southend United, 1994	£250,000
359.	Jackie Law from Airdrieonians, 1936	£1,500
360.	Rowan Alexander to St Mirren, 1983	£25,000

ANDY THOMSON

361.	1971
362.	Gillingham
363.	Aberdeen
364.	175
365.	114
366.	Stenhousemuir
367.	Queens Park Rangers
368.	Scottish Second Division Player of the Year
369.	Striker

370.   Partick Thistle (2003-04) and Falkirk (2004-06)

IAIN McCHESNEY

371.   1944

372.   Kello Rovers

373.   615

374.   Ayr United

375.   Greenock Morton

376.   Bobby Black

377.   79

378.   Jimmy McKinnell Junior

379.   Defender

380.   22 years (July 1960 to April 1982)

TED McMINN

381.   1962

382.   Kevin

383.   Rangers

384.   Winger

385.   68

386.   Meadowbank Thistle

387.   Glenafton Athletic

388.   5

389.   Derby County

390.   Slough Town

JIM PATTERSON

391.   'Big Jim'

392.   462

393.   Striker

394.   Dundee

395.   6

396.   Clyde

397.   251

398.   14

399.   Luncarty Juniors (Perthshire)

400.   False: he played just once, against The Army in 1953 at
       Hampden Park

WHICH TEAM ARE QUEENS PLAYING? – 1

401.   Falkirk

402.   Kilmarnock

403.   St Johnstone

404.   Dundee

405.   Aberdeen

406.   Rangers

407.   Stenhousemuir or East Stirlingshire

408.   Celtic

409.   Albion Rovers

410.   Dundee United

MATCH THE YEAR – 1

411.   The first ever Scottish League match
       under floodlights was played between
       Rangers and Queen of the South   1956

412.   Queen of the South were Scottish Cup
       runners-up to Rangers   2008

413.   Queens won the Potts Cup for the first time   1921

414.   John Connolly became Second Division
       Manager of the Season   2002

415.   Queens won the Algiers invitational tournament   1936

416.   Ally McLeod became manager of Queens   1991

417.   The first Queen of the South match-day
       programme was published   1933

418.	The lowest recorded attendance of 300 saw	
	Queens beat Alloa Athletic 1-0	1974
419.	Freddie Jenkins joined The Doonhamers	1947
420.	Scenes for the film A Shot at Glory were shot	
	at Palmerston Park	1999

JAMES 'JIM' THOMSON

421.	1971
422.	Clyde
423.	'JT'
424.	Stenhousemuir
425.	Central defender
426.	St Johnstone
427.	50
428.	Arbroath
429.	Clyde
430.	East Fife

MATCH THE YEAR – 2

431.	Queens reached the Scottish Challenge	
	Cup final for the first time	1997
432.	Goalkeeper Jimmy Coupland signed for Queens	1924
433.	Steve Tosh was born	1973
434.	Robert Harris joined The Doonhamers	2007
435.	Bernie Slaven played just two games for Queens	1983
436.	John O'Neill was awarded the Second	
	Division Player of the Season	2002
437.	Ian Dickson was born	1902
438.	Willie Fotheringham signed for The Doonhamers	1933
439.	Billy Houliston signed for Queens	1945
440.	David McNiven was born	1978

QUEENS V. STRANRAER

441.	1924
442.	8-0 to Queen of the South
443.	Scottish League Challenge Cup
444.	John O'Neil
445.	True
446.	11-1 to Queen of the South
447.	Steve Bowey
448.	True
449.	5-5
450.	Stevie Mallan

HAT-TRICKS

451.	Jackie Brown	4
452.	Ian Reid	5
453.	Jim Patterson	11
454.	Lex Law	1
455.	Tommy Bryce (Mark 2)	4
456.	Rowan Alexander	3
457.	Jimmy Robertson	2
458.	Bobby Black	3
459.	Willie Dougan	3
460.	Billy Houliston	2

CLUB HONOURS – 2

461.	Division 2 Runners-Up	1985/86
462.	Western League Champions	1922/23
463.	B&Q Cup Semi-Finalists	1991/92
464.	Bell's Cup (League Challenge Cup) Winners	2002/03
465.	Southern Counties League Cup Winners	1996/97
466.	Algiers Invitational Tournament Winners	1936
467.	Scottish Brewers Cup Winners	2006/07

468.	Scottish League South and West Runners-up	
	(Wartime League)	*1939/40*
469.	Border Cup Winners	*1991/92*
470.	Potts Cup Winners	*1961*

2006/07

471.	Partick Thistle
472.	Stephen Dobbie
473.	True: 2 draws and 8 defeats
474.	Ian McCall
475.	10
476.	John O'Neil and Stephen Dobbie
477.	Jamie McQuilken
478.	Ross County
479.	Airdrie United
480.	John O'Neil

LEAGUE POSITIONS – 3

481.	1988/89	14th in Division One
482.	1987/88	7th in Division One
483.	1986/87	10th in Division One
484.	1985/86	2nd in Division Two
485.	1984/85	8th in Division Two
486.	1983/84	6th in Division Two
487.	1982/83	7th in Division Two
488.	1981/82	14th in Division One
489.	1980/81	2nd in Division Two
490.	1979/80	13th in Division Two

CAPPED QUEENS

491.	Lex Law	2 Scottish Under-18 caps in 1965
492.	Peter Dickson	1 Scottish Under-23 cap in 1976

493.	Billy Houliston	3 Full Scottish caps in 1948 and 1949
494.	Ian Mitchell	1 Scottish Under-21 cap in 1979
495.	Chris Doig	1 Scottish Under-15 cap in 1997
496.	Keith Houliston	3 Scottish Amateur caps in 1970 and 1971
497.	Murray Landsborough	1 Scottish Army cap in 1945
498.	Thomas Baxter	1 Scottish Under-23 cap in 1956
499.	David Mathieson	3 Scottish Under-21 caps in 1997 and 1999
500.	Jim Patterson	1 Scottish cap in 1953

SCOTTISH LEAGUE CHALLENGE CUP RUNNERS-UP – 1997/98

501. Falkirk

502. Fir Park, Motherwell

503. David Mathieson, David Kennedy, Andy Aitken, George Rowe, Jim Thomson, Derek Townsley, Marc Cleeland, Tommy Bryce, Stevie Mallan, Ken Eadie and Des McKeown

504. Greenock Morton

505. Craig Flannigan and Stevie Mallan

506. Stevie Mallan

507. Inverness Caledonian Thistle

508. 2-0

509. Stirling Albion

510. Stevie Mallan

QUEENS V. ABERDEEN

511. True

512. 4-3 to Queen of the South

513. Steve Tosh, Paul Burns, Sean O'Connor and John Stewart

514. 1933

515. Scottish FA Cup

516. 5-4 to Aberdeen

517.   *George Hamilton*

518.   *True*

519.   *Craig Feroz*

520.   *1939*

WHERE DID THEY COME FROM? – 2

521.   *Allan Preston*   *St Johnstone*

522.   *George Farm*   *Blackpool*

523.   *Sean O'Connor*   *Annan Athletic*

524.   *Stewart Kean*   *St Mirren*

525.   *Bobby Black*   *East Fife*

526.   *Bobby Shearer*   *Rangers*

527.   *Neil Scally*   *Falkirk*

528.   *Phil Watson*   *Barnsley*

529.   *Gary Arbuckle*   *Clyde*

530.   *Ernie Bond*   *Carlisle United*

WHERE DID THEY GO? – 2

531.   *Stephen Grindlay*   *Ayr United*

532.   *Andy Aitken (first spell)*   *Gretna*

533.   *Steven Bell*   *Stirling Albion*

534.   *Sandy Hodge (first spell)*   *Stranraer*

535.   *Shaun Dillon*   *Stenhousemuir*

536.   *Tommy Lang*   *Ipswich Town*

537.   *Willie Gibson*   *Kilmarnock*

538.   *Bob McDermid*   *Aberdeen*

539.   *Derek Allan*   *Dumbarton*

540.   *Jimmy Brown*   *Carlisle United*

WHICH TEAM ARE QUEENS PLAYING? – 2

541.   *Peterhead*

542.   *Raith Rovers*

543.   **St Mirren**

544.   **Dunfermline Athletic**

545.   **Motherwell**

546.   **Hamilton Academical**

547.   **Airdrie United**

548.   **Heart of Midlothian**

549.   **Hibernian**

550.   **Stranraer**

LEAGUE GOALSCORERS - 1

551.	**Neil Martin**	**33**
552.	**Andy Thomson**	**93**
553.	**Iain McChesney**	**67**
554.	**Paddy Atkinson**	**5**
555.	**Billy Reid**	**22**
556.	**Stephen Dobbie**	**47**
557.	**Ken Eadie**	**17**
558.	**Jocky Dempster**	**78**
559.	**Sam English**	**8**
560.	**Willie McLean**	**10**

DAVE HALLIDAY

561.   **True**

562.   **1901**

563.   **13**

564.   **Leicester City**

565.   **St Mirren**

566.   **Sunderland**

567.   **373**

568.   **Outside left**

569.   **Yeovil and Petters United**

570.   **George Hamilton**

PAUL BURNS

571.   2000

572.   Midfielder

573.   Ross County

574.   1984

575.   Eric Paton

576.   Dunfermline Athletic

577.   28

578.   True

579.   1 (Steve Tosh, Sean O'Connor and John Stewart scored the other goals)

580.   Burnsy

ANDY AITKEN

581.   Robert

582.   Norman Blount

583.   Gretna

584.   260

585.   Ayr United

586.   1978

587.   Defender

588.   Ian McCall

589.   4

590.   Annan Athletic

ALAN DAVIDSON

591.   1960

592.   364

593.   Airdrieonians

594.   Floreat Athena

595.   Goalkeeper

596.   Celtic

597. None

598. 2 (1982-88 and 1989-94)

599. Albion Rovers

600. 312

PLAYER OF THE YEAR – 2

601.	Jim Thomson	2005
602.	Stuart Gordon	1991
603.	Billy Reid	1988
604.	Crawford Boyd	1974
605.	Mike Jackson	1968
606.	Steve Bowey	2003
607.	Nobby Clark	1978
608.	Alan Davidson	1984
609.	Tommy Bryce (Mark 2)	1995
610.	Iain McChesney	1970

QUEENS V. CELTIC

611. 1927

612. True

613. 1-0 to Queen of the South

614. 1 (1 draw and 4 defeats)

615. Scottish League Cup (3rd round)

616. 4-3 to Queen of the South

617. True: 3-2 at home and 1-0 away

618. 2-1 to Celtic

619. Celtic (they finished 5th and Queens finished 16th)

620. True: 4-3 at home and 2-1 away

2004/05

621. St Johnstone

622. 14

623. *Richie Barnard*
624. *Derek Lyle*
625. *True*
626. *Stephen Payne*
627. *Steve Bowey*
628. *Falkirk*
629. *12*
630. *Stuart Lovell*

WHICH TEAM ARE QUEENS PLAYING? – 3

631. *Forfar Athletic*
632. *Brechin City*
633. *Arbroath*
634. *Montrose*
635. *Queens Park*
636. *Greenock Morton*
637. *Clyde*
638. *Dumbarton*
639. *East Fife*
640. *Ayr United*

LEAGUE GOALSCORERS – 2

641.	*Darren Henderson*	*9*
642.	*Rowan Alexander*	*71*
643.	*Sandy Hodge*	*1*
644.	*Steven Bowey*	*16*
645.	*Alex Burke*	*13*
646.	*John O'Neill*	*58*
647.	*Ian Cochrane*	*2*
648.	*Emilio Jaconelli*	*3*
649.	*Sean O'Connor*	*33*
650.	*Peter Weatherson*	*38*

HUGHIE GALLACHER

651. 1903
652. 19
653. Kilpatrick
654. 23
655. 4
656. Centre forward
657. Airdrieonians
658. 463
659. Gateshead
660. Newcastle United

NEIL MARTIN

661. Alloa Athletic
662. Italy
663. 61
664. 1940
665. Hibernian
666. 3
667. Forward
668. Sunderland
669. True: 101 in Scotland and 115 in England
670. St Patrick's Athletic

ROWAN ALEXANDER

671. Samuel
672. Billy McLaren
673. Gretna
674. Greenock Morton
675. Striker
676. Mark Shanks
677. 154

678. *Gretna*

679. *Brentford (1984-86)*

680. *True: all with Gretna, SL1 - 2006-07, SL2 - 2005-06 and SL3 - 2004-05*

JOHN 'JOCKY' DEMPSTER

681. *Winger*

682. *98*

683. *St Mirren*

684. *Muirkirk*

685. *355*

686. *Allan Ball, Iain McChesney and Crawford Boyd*

687. *Clyde*

688. *1948*

689. *Berwick Rangers*

690. *Mr John Watson*

WHO AM I?

691. *Jackie Oakes*

692. *Ian Dickson*

693. *Roy Henderson*

694. *Willie Savage*

695. *Dennis Wyness*

696. *Willie Ferguson*

697. *Crawford Boyd*

698. *Stephen McKenna*

699. *Billy Houliston*

700. *Dougie Sharpe*

LEAGUE POSITIONS – 4

701. *1978/79*   *14th in Division One*

702. *1977/78*   *12th in Division One*

703.	1976/77	9th in Division One
704.	1975/76	10th in Division One
705.	1974/75	2nd in Division Two
706.	1973/74	4th in Division Two
707.	1972/73	11th in Division Two
708.	1971/72	7th in Division Two
709.	1970/71	11th in Division Two
710.	1969/70	3rd in Division Two

CLUB HONOURS – 3

711.	B.P. Youth Cup Runners-Up	1985/86
712.	Scottish Cup Semi-Finalists	1949/50
713.	Southern Counties Charity Cup Winners	1937
714.	Southern Counties Cup Winners	2004
715.	Scottish Brewers Cup Winners	2001/02
716.	Scottish Cup Runners-Up	2007/08
717.	Scottish League Cup Semi-Finalists	1950/51
718.	Southern Counties Cup Winners	1987
719.	Division 2 Runners-up	1980/81
720.	Scottish League Cup Semi-Finalists	1960/61

2005/06

721.	St Mirren
722.	True: 1 draw, 3 defeats
723.	8th
724.	Andy Aitken
725.	10
726.	True: 1 win and 2 draws
727.	Garry Wood
728.	St Johnstone
729.	Graham Weir
730.	7

WHICH TEAM ARE QUEENS PLAYING? – 4

731.   Inverness Caledonian Thistle

732.   Partick Thistle

733.   Livingston

734.   Stirling Albion

735.   Alloa Athletic

736.   Cowdenbeath

737.   Ross County

738.   Annan Athletic

739.   Berwick Rangers

740.   Elgin City

TOMMY BRYCE (MARK 2)

741.   1960

742.   Kilmarnock

743.   297

744.   Man of the Match in the 1997 Challenge Cup final

745.   95

746.   Partick Thistle

747.   Forward

748.   Stranraer

749.   Nobby Clark

750.   Clydebank (1987-89 and 1992-93) and Stranraer (1982-85 and 2000-01)

GEORGE HAMILTON

751.   1917

752.   Inside forward

753.   Irvine Meadow

754.   31

755.   Aberdeen

756.   5

757. 9

758. Belguim

759. Hamilton Academical

760. Dave Halliday

JIMMY ROBERTSON

761. 1955

762. 342

763. Stenhousemuir

764. Motherwell

765. Left wing

766. 77

767. Greenock Morton (1987-89) and Clydebank (1989)

768. Rangers

769. 400

770. Stranraer

LEAGUE GOALSCORERS – 3

771.	Murray Henderson	1
772.	Tommy O'Hara	9
773.	Neil MacFarlane	1
774.	Drew Busby	11
775.	Mick Oliver	2
776.	Colin Harris	9
777.	Harry Hood	4
778.	Alex Totten	6
779.	Frank McGarvey	2
780.	Tommy McCulloch	4

LEAGUE POSITIONS – 5

781.	1968/69	5th in Division Two
782.	1967/68	6th in Division Two

783.	1966/67	9th in Division Two
784.	1965/66	3rd in Division Two
785.	1964/65	3rd in Division Two
786.	1963/64	17th in Division One
787.	1962/63	15th in Division One
788.	1961/62	2nd in Division Two
789.	1960/61	5th in Division Two
790.	1959/60	3rd in Division Two

PLAYER OF THE YEAR – 3

791.	Jim Kerr	1964
792.	Allan Ball	1965
793.	Billy Sim	1987
794.	Jimmy Robertson	1980
795.	Gary Fraser	1989
796.	Steve Mallan	2000
797.	Alan Gray	2002
798.	George Cloy	1985
799.	David Kennedy	1996
800.	Billy Collings	1966

NOTES

NOTES

OTHER BOOKS BY CHRIS COWLIN:

* Celebrities' Favourite Football Teams

* The British TV Sitcom Quiz Book

* The Cricket Quiz Book

* The Gooners Quiz Book

* The Horror Film Quiz Book

* The Official Aston Villa Quiz Book

* The Official Birmingham City Quiz Book

* The Official Brentford Quiz Book

* The Official Bristol Rovers Quiz Book

* The Official Burnley Quiz Book

* The Official Bury Quiz Book

* The Official Carlisle United Quiz Book

* The Official Carry On Quiz Book

* The Official Chesterfield Football Club Quiz Book

* The Official Colchester United Quiz Book

* The Official Coventry City Quiz Book

* The Official Doncaster Rovers Quiz Book

* The Official Greenock Morton Quiz Book

* The Official Heart of Midlothian Quiz Book

* The Official Hereford United Quiz Book

* The Official Hull City Quiz Book

* The Official Ipswich Town Quiz Book

OTHER BOOKS BY CHRIS COWLIN:

* The Official Leicester City Quiz Book

* The Official Macclesfield Town Quiz Book

* The Official Norwich City Football Club Quiz

* The Official Notts County Quiz Book

* The Official Peterborough United Quiz Book

* The Official Port Vale Quiz Book

* The Official Queen of the South Quiz Book

* The Official Rochdale AFC Quiz Book

* The Official Rotherham United Quiz Book

* The Official Sheffield United Quiz Book

* The Official Shrewsbury Town Quiz Book

* The Official Stockport County Quiz Book

* The Official Walsall Football Club Quiz Book

* The Official Watford Football Club Quiz Book

* The Official West Bromwich Albion Quiz Book

* The Official Wolves Quiz Book

* The Official Yeovil Town Quiz Book

* The Reality Television Quiz Book

* The Southend United Quiz Book

* The Spurs Quiz Book

* The Sunderland AFC Quiz Book

* The Ultimate Derby County Quiz Book

* The West Ham United Quiz Book

www.apexpublishing.co.uk